Go For It Maths!
KEY STAGE 1

Let's Measure It

Practise and Learn with Games and Activities

By Mike Askew

RuBY TUESDAY BOOKS

Tips for Doing Maths with Your Child

- Find a quiet place to work with no distractions. Turn off the TV, music and screens.

- The activities in this book have been designed to help children learn about measuring while playing games and having fun. There are specific tips relating to each activity on pages 30–32.

- Do praise your child for specific mathematical things they do. If you say, *"That was really smart when you used the ruler to check that measurement"*, it will be more effective than *"You are clever"*.

- Do let your child teach you. Listen to how they are trying to do the maths and help them refine what they are doing before rushing to show them **your way**.

- Do treat getting stuck as a positive experience. **Yet** is a powerful word. *"I can't do it!"* can be turned around by saying, *"You can't do it – yet!"*

- Do stop work and put an activity aside if your child gets frustrated. When you come back to the activity the following day, they are likely to have fresh ideas.

- Avoid saying things such as *"Don't worry. I was never any good at maths."* Help your child develop a **can-do** view of learning maths.

Above all, treat all the activities playfully and enjoy them together.

Contents

Measuring Me! 4

Best Foot Forward 6

Biggest Smile 7

Make Marble Weights 8

Ten to a Kilo 9

That's Handy! 10

Roll 'Em 12

Leaf Prints..13

Timelines 14

Fill a Box..16

Order & Check 17

Pour & Check 18

Make a Measuring Jug.................................20

My Crazy Day 22

Just a Minute! 24

Calendar Patterns 25

Victoria's Sponge 26

Ruler Race...28

Tips for Maths Success................................30

Measuring Me!

You will need:
- A ball of thin string or thick wool
- Scissors
- A helper

Are You Square?

You can find out if you're square by doing some measuring with a helper.

Get your helper to measure your height with a piece of string.

Next put your arms out wide. Your body span is the length from the tip of one finger to the other.

Get your helper to measure your body span with string.

If the piece of string for your height is the same length as the piece of string for your body span, you are square.

How square are you?

Measure your best friends or your family. Who is the most square?

4

Get Ready

You will need:
- A ball of thin string or thick wool
- Scissors
- A helper

Number 3 says:

Three times around your head is about the same as your height!

Let's check it out!

Ask your helper to wrap a length of string around your head three times.

They should make a mark on the string where it meets up with the start of the string.

Take the string off your head and cut it at the mark.

Compare the length of this string with the string that measured your height.

Was Number 3 right?

Go For It!

Compare other parts of your body. For example, how does the length from the tip of your middle finger to your elbow compare with the length of your foot?

Best Foot Forward

Get Ready

You will need:
- Paper and a pen or pencil

Try measuring the length of your bed with your feet.

Pigeon Steps

Start at the end of your bed and measure its length in pigeon steps.

Put the heel of one foot so it touches the toes of the foot behind.

Keep pigeon-stepping and count how many steps.

You can make a tally of your steps so you don't lose count.

Strides

Now measure the length of your bed in strides, or big steps.

Did it take more pigeon steps or strides to measure your bed? Why?

How many pigeon steps do you think it will take to cross the room? How about strides?

Write down your predictions and then check them.

GO For It!

Get an adult to measure your bed and room using pigeon steps and strides. Did they get the same numbers as you?

Biggest Smile

Get Ready

You will need:
- Paper and a pen or pencil
- Measuring tools, such as a ruler, tape measure or string

How can you measure a smile?

You can use a piece of string.

Who has the biggest smile in your family?

You could hold a piece of paper to a person's' mouth. Mark the corners of their smile on the paper and then measure from mark to mark with a tape measure.

Can you think of another way to measure a smile?

Now measure your family's smiles. Use the same method to measure each smile so you can compare your results.

Who has the biggest smile?

You could take a close-up photo on a phone, print out the photo and then measure the smile with a ruler.

Go For It!

Measure people's mouths when they are not smiling.

Whose mouth widens up the most when they smile?

Make Marble Weights

Get Ready

People used to use weights called pounds and ounces.

You will need:
- 15 marbles or small stones
- 4 small sandwich bags
- Sticky tape
- Paper and a pen or pencil

Weights

Scales

1 ounce

2 ounce

4 ounce

8 ounce

Ounce weights were made to be used on scales.

You can make a set of weights using marbles.

1 Put one marble in a sandwich bag and seal the bag with sticky tape.

2 Make three other bags, one bag with 2 marbles, a bag with 4 marbles and a bag with 8 marbles.

3 Now use your four bags to solve these challenges.

Can you use your bags of marble weights to make a weight of 7 marbles?

Can you make a total weight of 13 marbles?

Can you make all possible weights from 1 marble to 15 marbles by combining your bags?

Ten to a Kilo

Get Ready

You will need:
- Kitchen scales
- A kilogram bag of flour or sugar
- Objects from around the kitchen

Put the bag of flour or sugar on the scales.

Look at the scales and notice what the scales are showing when something weighs 1 kilogram.

1000.0⁹

This digital scale is showing 1000 grams. That's the same as 1 kilogram.

Can you find 10 different things in the kitchen that together weigh 1 kilogram?

Can you find 20 different things that together weigh 1 kilogram?

That's Handy!

You will need:
- Paper and a pen or pencil
- Thin wool or thick cotton
- Scissors
- Some water

Round and Round Your Hand

Place your hand on the paper with your fingers closed and draw around your hand.

How far would an ant crawl if it went all the way around the outside of your hand?

You can use the wool to find out.

Carefully place the wool around the hand outline on the paper. It will stay in place if you wet it with a little water.

Cut the wool so you have a piece that's the same length as the distance around your hand.

How far would an ant crawl if it went all the way around the outside of your hand with your fingers spread apart?

Now draw around your hand with your fingers spread apart.

Measure the outline with another piece of wool.

Which length is the longer?

Why do you think this is?

Four's Fantastic Facts

The distance around the outside of a shape is called the **perimeter**.

You will need:
- The outlines of your hands from page 10
- Lots of counters, buttons or dried beans

Carefully fill the hand shape with counters. Make sure they are placed close together.

Count how many you use and record your answer.

Cover Up

Take the outline of your hand with the fingers closed.

Now use counters to fill the outline of your hand with the fingers spread apart.

Count how many counters you use and record this answer.

How many counters did you use to fill each hand?

Why do you think you got the results you did?

Four's Fantastic Facts

We call the space a shape covers the **area** of the shape.

Go For It!

Use wool and counters to investigate the perimeter and area of your foot.

11

Roll 'Em

Get Ready

You will need:
- Some big books
- A collection of objects that roll
- A tape measure
- Paper and a pen or pencil

To play "Roll 'Em" you will need plenty of space. A hallway is a good place to set up your investigation.

1. Make a ramp by leaning a book against a stack of other books.

2. Hold one of your objects at the top of the ramp. Let go and allow it to continue rolling until it stops.

3. Now examine each of your other objects.

   Do you think each one will roll for a longer or a shorter distance than the first object?

   Which object do you think will roll the furthest?

4. Record your predictions and then test them.

5. If you wish, measure in centimetres or metres how far from the bottom of the ramp each object rolls.

GO For It!

Make your ramp higher or lower by changing the number of books in the stack.

How does changing the height of the ramp affect how far things roll?

Leaf Prints

You will need:
- 2 leaves that are a different size and shape
- 2 sheets of paper that are the same size
- Paints and paintbrushes

Let's investigate "area" by making some leaf prints.

1. To print with a leaf, paint it with a thin coat of paint.

2. Press the painted side down onto the sheet of paper. You may be able to print two or three times before reapplying the paint.

3. Try to cover as much of the paper as possible with leaf prints. But do not let your leaf prints overlap.

   How many leaf prints did it take to cover the sheet of paper?

4. Now take the second sheet of paper and your second leaf.

   How many prints of this leaf do you think it will take to cover the paper?

5. Check your guess by printing with your leaf all over the paper. But remember, don't overlap the prints.

Go For It!

If you have finger paints try covering a sheet of paper with handprints. Try it with your fingers closed. Then try it with your fingers spread open.

13

Timelines

You will need:
- Sheets of paper (one for every year of your age)
- Sticky tape
- Coloured pens or pencils
- Photos of you and your family

My Story

Make a timeline of your life.

1 Label a sheet of paper with the year you were born. Label the next sheet with the year after that. Keep going until you reach this year.

2 On the paper for this year, draw a picture of yourself now or stick on a photo.

3 Now work backwards, drawing pictures or sticking photos for things that have happened to you in each year.

4 Finally, stick your sheets of paper together to make one long strip.

2011

The year you were born.

2012

Moving to a new house.

2013

A new brother or sister

2014

A new pet

2015

First day at school

2016

A birthday party

2017

Going on a plane for the first time.

2018

You today

5 Use your timeline to tell the story of your life to your family, friends or teacher.

Get Ready

You will need:
- 12 sheets of paper
- Sticky tape
- Pencils, pens or paints

Take your first sheet of paper and label it January. Then label the second sheet February.

1 Keep going and write each month of the year on a separate sheet of paper.

2 Now join your sheets of paper together to make one long strip.

3 Draw or paint something that you do in each month and make a timeline of your year.

What kinds of things do you do in each month of the year?

You might build a snowman in January.

Perhaps you visit Grandma for her birthday in June or go on holiday in August.

In October it's time to dress up for Halloween!

Fill a Box

Get Ready

You will need:
- A small box (a ring box, matchbox, stock cube or raisins box)

You can only have one of each type of thing in the box.

Here are some ideas to get you started!

A paper clip

A screw

A single rice grain

A bead

A flower petal

A cornflake

A button

A grain of salt

When your box is full, count how many different items it was able to hold.

Four's Fantastic Facts

We call how much a box or other container can hold its **capacity**.

GO For It!

Make this a family competition. Everyone has the same size box and a week to fill it. The winner is the person with the most number of different things in their box!

Order & Check

Can you put things in order by how much they weigh? Let's go for it and find out!

Get Ready

You will need:

- A collection of 6 food objects from the kitchen, such as boxes, packets or jars
- Paper and a pen or pencil
- Kitchen scales

1 Collect together six things from the kitchen cupboards. Look for things that are different sizes and weights.

2 Pick up two of your objects and hold one in each hand.

Which feels heavier?

Now swap hands.

Does the same object still feel heavier?

3 Keep comparing pairs of objects until you think you have found the heaviest one. Put that object to one side. Write or draw what it is on your sheet of paper.

Now use the kitchen scales to check if you got the order right.

4 Now decide which object you think is the next heaviest. Put it beside the first object. Record what it is.

5 Keep going until you have all the objects in order, from what you think is the heaviest to the lightest.

Pour & Check

Begin by collecting six containers from around your kitchen.

Get Ready

You will need:
- A collection of 6 containers from the kitchen
- Paper and a pen or pencil
- Water
- An egg cup or empty yogurt pot

Look for containers that are different shapes and will hold different amounts of water.

Saucepan

Cup

Empty glass jar

Vase

Plastic box

Jug

1 Take two of your containers. Look at them carefully.

If you pour water into each container, which do you think will hold more water?

2 Keep looking and comparing pairs of containers until you think you have found the one that will hold the most water.

I think the jug will hold the most water!

3 Put that container to one side. Write or draw what it is on your paper.

4 Now decide which container you think is the next size down. Put it beside the first object. Record what it is.

Keep going until you have all the containers in order, from the one you think will hold the most water to the one you think will hold the least water.

Container 1   Container 2   Container 3   Container 4   Container 5   Container 6

Now check if you got the order right!

5 Fill Container 1 with water.

Then pour water from Container 1 to fill your egg cup.

Make a tally to show you have filled the egg cup once.

Container 1
Jug

|

6 Empty the egg cup.
Fill it again from Container 1.
Make another tally.

Keep pouring and making tallies until Container 1 is empty.

How many egg cups of water did Container 1 hold?

Container 1
Jug

|||| |||| ||||

|||| ||

7 Now use the egg cup to find out how much water each of the other five containers will hold.

8 When you've tested all six containers, look at your tallies.

Did you have the containers in the right order?

19

Make a Measuring Jug

Get Ready

Get ready to do some measuring using your own homemade measuring jug!

You will need:
- An empty plastic bottle (one with smooth sides is best)
- Scissors
- An adult helper
- Sheet of paper
- Sticky tape
- An empty yogurt pot
- A black marker pen

1 Ask an adult to cut off the top part of the bottle.

Keep both parts of the bottle. You don't need the cap.

Cut here

2 Cut a strip of paper and tape it to the side of the bottle.

3 If you wish, you can turn the top part of the bottle upside-down and sit it in the bottom part to create a funnel.

4 Now fill the yogurt pot with water. Pour the water into the bottle.

Mark on the paper the place the water comes up to. This is level 1.

5 Fill the yogurt pot again and pour it into the bottle. Mark this as level 2.

20

6 Keep refilling the yogurt pot and pouring water into the bottle. Mark the level each time.

When the bottle is full pour away the water.

Four's Fantastic Facts

You have made your own measuring jug, or **measuring cylinder**. The numbers on the side of the cylinder are called a **scale**.

Go For It!

Now you can use your measuring cylinder to do some measuring.

Find 3 containers:

How many yogurt pots of water does each container hold?

In turn, fill each container with water. Then pour the water into your measuring cylinder. Look at the scale and read off the measurement.

My Crazy Day

Get Ready

You will need:
- A large sheet of paper
- Scissors
- Coloured pens and pencils

What things do you do every day? What would happen if you had a mixed-up crazy day?

1 Take your sheet of paper and fold it in half. Then fold it in half again. And finally fold it in half one more time.

Next, unfold your paper and you should have made 8 sections.

2 Number the sections from 1 to 8.

| 1 | 2 | 3 | 4 |
| 5 | 6 | 7 | 8 |

At what time do you do these things?

3 Now think about the things you do from getting up in the morning to going to bed at night.

For example:
- You get out of bed.
- You get washed.
- You get dressed.
- You eat breakfast.

You can download a series of clocks here:
www.rubytuesdaybooks.com/goforit

4 Choose 8 things that you do in a day.

5 Draw a picture for each thing you have chosen. Draw one thing in each box on your paper. You can also draw a clock that shows the time.

6 Cut up your paper into 8 separate pieces.

Here are some ideas for the kinds of things you could draw.

1

I wake up.

2

I eat breakfast.

3

I walk to school.

4

I eat my lunch.

5

I go swimming.

6

I eat my dinner.

7

I brush my teeth.

8

I go to bed.

GO For It!

Now it's time to play "Crazy Day".

Put the pieces of paper face down on the table and mix them up.

Turn over the pieces of paper one at a time and tell the story of your crazy day.

For example:
I woke up.
Then I ate my dinner.
Then I walked to school.
Then I ate my breakfast!

Just a Minute!

What can you do in a minute?

Get Ready

You will need:
- Paper and a pen or pencil
- A mobile phone with a timer

You can make a star by drawing a triangle. Then draw another upside-down triangle on top.

You could try drawing lots of stars.

Get ready for your challenge by practising drawing stars.

STOPWATCH

45

START STOP

Now set the timer on the phone for one minute and GO FOR IT!

How many stars did you draw?

Try again! Did you manage to draw more stars the second time?

Four's Fantastic Facts

There are 60 seconds in 1 minute.
There are 60 minutes in 1 hour.

GO For It !

Test your family and friends. Who is the fastest one-minute-star-drawer?

How many times can you write your name in one minute?

How high can you count in one minute?

24

Calendar Patterns

On your calendar, draw a square around four dates.

You will need:
- A calendar page showing a full month (it can be an old one)
- A pen or pencil

Add the date in the top left-hand corner of your square to the date in the bottom right-hand corner.

$11 + 19 = 30$

Now add the date in the top right-hand corner of your square to the date in the bottom left-hand corner.

$12 + 18 = \,?$

What do you notice?

Try drawing another square around four different dates.

Does the same thing happen?

SEPTEMBER 2018

	SUN	MON	TUE	WED	THU	FRI	SAT
35							1
36	2	3	4	5	6	7	8
37	9	10	11	12	13	14	15
38	16	17	18	19	20	21	
39	23	24	25	26	27	2	29
40	30						

GO FOR It!

What happens if you add the opposite corners on a three-by-three square?

SEPTEMBER 2018

	SUN	MON	TUE	WED	THU	FRI	SAT
							1
	2	3	4	5	6	7	8
	9	10	11	12	13	14	15
	16	17	18	19	20	21	22
	23	24	25	26	27	28	29
	30						

Victoria's Sponge

Get Ready

You will need:
- 4 eggs
- Soft butter
- Caster sugar
- Self-raising flour
- A teaspoon of vanilla essence
- Kitchen scales
- A mixing bowl
- A wooden spoon
- A little butter for greasing
- 2 17-cm cake tins
- Oven gloves
- Raspberry jam and a spoon
- An adult helper

Look at Grandmother Victoria's sponge cake recipe. How does she know what quantity of each of the ingredients are needed?

Victoria's Sponge Recipe
4 eggs
butter
caster sugar
flour

Grandmother Victoria knows a special measuring trick!

1. First weigh the eggs. These eggs weigh 270 grams.

2. Now measure out the same weight of butter as the weight of the eggs.

3. Next, measure out the same weight again of sugar and flour.

Great measuring! You're all set to get baking.

How to Make Victoria's Sponge

1. Ask an adult to help you switch the oven to 170° C.

2. Grease the cake tins with a little butter to stop your sponges sticking to the tins.

3. Put the butter and sugar into the mixing bowl. Beat the ingredients with a wooden spoon until the mixture is light and fluffy.

4. Add the eggs one at a time, beating them into the mixture.

5. If you wish, you can add a teaspoon of vanilla essence. Stir it in.

6. Add the flour to the mixture and gently stir it into the other ingredients.

7. Divide the sponge mixture equally between the two cake tins.

8. Ask an adult to help you put the cakes into the oven. Bake them for about 25 minutes.

GO For It!

When your sponges have cooled, you can sandwich them together with jam. Put a teaspoon of jam on the bottom sponge and spread it. How many spoons of jam do you estimate it will take to cover the sponge with a thick jammy layer?

27

Ruler Race

Get Ready

You will need:
- Paper and pens or pencils
- 3 dice
- 2 rulers
- A mobile phone with a timer

Before you begin playing, each player draws a chart to record their Ruler Race measurements.

	Ruby		
Dice Total	Object	Measurement	Score

1 Next, Player One (Ruby) throws the three dice and adds up the score:

$$5 + 5 + 3 = 13$$

2 Player One records their dice total on their chart. Then they throw the dice four more times, recording the total each time.

	Ruby		
Dice Total	Object	Measurement	Score
13			
3			
8			
18			
5			

3 Next, Player Two (Sam) throws the dice five times and records their totals.

4 Now, the players have 5 minutes to find 5 items that are the length of their dice scores in centimetres.

The players cannot measure the items during their search, but must estimate if the objects are the correct length.

> *For example, Ruby must find items that are 13 cm, 3 cm, 8 cm, 18 cm and 5 cm long.*

5 The timer is set, and the race begins!

6 When the time is up, the players use their rulers to measure the objects they've found.

GLUE

← 7 cm →

← 3 cm →

← 11 cm →

10 cm

← 8 cm →

If an object is the exact measurement or within 1 cm of the dice score in either direction, that counts as a point. If there is more than 1 cm difference, no point is scored.

	Ruby		
Dice Total	Object	Measurement	Score
13	Book	16 cm	✗
3	Coin	3 cm	✓
8	Playing card	8 cm	✓
18	Pencil	11 cm	✗
5	Glue stick	7 cm	✗

	Sam		
Dice Total	Object	Measurement	Score
18	Book	19 cm	✓
3	Lego	3 cm	✓
10	Teddy	10 cm	✓
12	Glasses	13 cm	✓
7	Purse	11 cm	✗

Sam is the winner of this game with 4 points!

You can also try playing Ruler Race with four dice or just two dice.

Tips for Maths Success

Pages 4—5: Measuring Me!

Measuring is all about comparing. In "Are You Square?" your child gets to compare their height with their body span without needing to use any units. You and your child might enjoy looking up Da Vinci's Vitruvian Man online — perfectly square!

Page 6: Best Foot Forward

A core idea for children to understand in measuring is that the larger the unit the fewer of them will be needed. This activity explores this inverse relationship in two different ways: by comparing pigeon steps with strides and your child's measurements with yours.

Page 7: Biggest Smile

Measuring things in real-life is often more difficult than measuring on the page of a book. This is a light-hearted activity to encourage your child (and you) to find some inventive ways of measuring something that's not usually or easily measured.

Page 8: Make Marble Weights

If you have a set of balance scales your child can use this to put their bags of marbles on one side and weigh out quantities of rice or dried pasta on the other. Ask around to find out if anyone you know has an old set of ounce weights for your child to investigate.

Page 9: Ten to a Kilo

Having a sense of what a kilogram "feels like" provides a good benchmark for estimating weights. Follow up this activity when you go shopping — does a cabbage weigh more or less than a kilogram? What about a bag of onions?

Pages 10—11: That's Handy!

Children often get confused about the difference between area (the amount of flat surface something covers) and perimeter (the length around the outside of an area). These activities provide the opportunity to introduce these ideas in a fun and informal way. Your child should discover that the perimeter of their hand is longer when their fingers are splayed out, but the area stays about the same.

Page 12: Roll 'Em

Your child can also try investigating the distance an object travels from different starting points on the ramp. They could also try attaching some cargo (such as plasticine) to a toy car to see how this affects the distance it rolls. Talk to your child about "fair tests". For example, making sure that the objects start at the same place on the ramp when they are being compared.

Page 13: Leaf Prints

Area is a measure that children usually learn later than length or weight. Print-making activities are a good way to help them get a sense of covering a surface with a repeated unit — a key part of understanding area.

Pages 14—15: Timelines

Making a timeline of their personal life history or of the things they do over the course of a year will help your child start to think about time. It will also help them to understand how to put events into chronological order. Making timelines is also a great way to help children recognise and use language relating to dates, months and years.

Page 16: Fill a Box

Capacity is a difficult measure. This challenge provides a way of talking about the capacity of a box. It also helps your child understand the idea that even something as small as a matchbox can sound as though it is very large if the things being used to measure it are very small.

Page 17: Order & Check

Length is the easiest measure because we can often see which is longer. I do not need a ruler to decide if I am taller or shorter than someone. But impressions can be deceiving when it comes to weight. A small box or other container may be heavier than a large one. Putting items from around the kitchen in order of weight will help your child's understanding of what measured properties are all about.

Pages 18—19: Pour & Check

Again, impressions can be deceiving when it comes to capacity. For example, a tall thin vase may hold less water than a short wide bowl. Putting items from around the kitchen in order of how much water they hold will help develop your child's understanding of capacity and volume.

Pages 20—21: Make a Measuring Jug

Creating a measuring scale in this way will help your child understand how measuring involves repeatedly using the same unit. Challenge your child to use their device to measure out set quantities — for example, 3 yogurt cartons of water or 4 yogurt cartons of uncooked rice.

Pages 22—23: My Crazy Day

Talking about and putting in order pictures of everyday activities provides your child with the opportunity to develop the language associated with time and the order in which things happen. If your child is not yet telling the time, simply draw the different activities without adding clocks but use time-related words such as morning, afternoon and evening.

Page 24: Just a Minute!

Help your child get a sense of the duration of a minute by challenging them to get better at a simple task. Encourage them to be creative and to think about other one-minute challenges they could try.

Page 25: Calendar Patterns

Calendars are a rich source of number patterns. The answer to the two sums should be the same. By checking if this always works, your child will get plenty of addition practice.

Pages 26—27: Victoria's Sponge

This activity works well if you have access to some old-fashioned balance scales. Put the eggs on one side and measure out the other ingredients on the other side. If you have digital scales or scales with a circular dial, weigh the eggs, get your child to write down the result and use this measurement to weigh out equal amounts of the butter, sugar and flour.

Pages 28—29: Ruler Race

This fun game gives your child plenty of practise at adding, estimating lengths and measuring with a ruler. It will also help give them a sense of how long a time period, such as five minutes, will last. Players will find that an object such as a playing card or book has sides of different lengths. Therefore, it might not be helpful for the measurement they originally intended, but could be useful for one of the other numbers they are trying to find. The more they play, the better their estimating skills will become. If they enjoy playing Ruler Race it can be made more challenging with a shorter time allowed for the search or different numbers of dice to potentially give bigger or much smaller measurements to find.